For over seventy years,
a little boy inside me has been nagging me to write this.
I hope he's happy now.

To Dorothy,
All the best to you,
always

FLYING GRASSHOPPERS & DIVING BOMBERS.

I felt the heat of the sun on my knees through the holes in my worn overalls.
The buzz from a large flying grasshopper broke the otherwise perfect silence.
I sat frozen in place as the grasshopper boldly settled on the back of my hand.
All six legs dug in for a better grip. I stared wide-eyed as he ground up weed clippings in his mouth then regurgitated "tobacco juice " on my wrist.

I was knee deep in nature. In a place we reverently called " Kritts field."
It was contentment I would never feel again.

The neighborhood was mostly Germans, all transplants from Europe, all out of their comfort zone adjusting to a new place some could barely pronounce. "America."
We were the only Italians.
Our customs were very different but we all had one thing in common.
Poverty.

I watched as old Mr. Schmidke sat motionless on his front porch. His suspenders dangled loosely at his sides. His tired eyes stared blankly at the horizon. Cigarette smoke curled slowly up his leathered face. Loose ashes tumbled down his yellowed undershirt.

I stared as his foundry hardened hand poured a shot from the nearby schnapps bottle. As he raised the shot glass to his lips it became obvious that two fingers were missing. Alcohol was an important staple in our neighborhood. But it never mixed well with operating a punch press at the local factory.

I never saw Mr. Schmidke smile. He barely ever uttered a word.

Why so solemn ? So absorbed ?

I didn't realize until years later that while I watched grasshoppers buzz peacefully over Kritts field, Adolph Hitler's menacing Luftwaffe was filling the skies over Mr. Schmidke's homeland.

War clouds were building .

The world as we knew it was about to change.

VINO & WEINER SCHNITZEL.

Mrs. Wagner spoke with a heavy German accent, deep guttural sounds unlike the "sing song" sounds of Italian I heard at home. I watched as she clipped her already perfect hedges.

She always wore a wide brimmed sun hat with a ribbon that she tied under her tightly clenched jaw. Her left eye having no pupil, resembled a hard boiled egg. This made it difficult to read her face, even her smile confused me. Was she simply offering the days pleasantries when she smiled, or was it a smirk of complete disdain because she caught me rummaging around in her prize flower bed looking for an errant fly ball last week ?

It was well beyond my seven year old comprehension.

Although, when she trained her good eye at my groin area and gave the hugh clippers a quick decisive snap, it became clear.

The clean smell of Fels Naptha soap filled the air as I approached the Brittenfeld house on the other side of the street. Lydia, another German neighbor, was on her hands and knees scrubbing the public sidewalk in front of her house. She had a stout tightly packed frame. Her sturdy arms tapered down to tiny raw red fingertips. The soapy water covered the scrub brush giving the

impression that she was scrubbing the pavement bare handed. I cringed at the grinding sound.

Lydia rose to her knees, wiped the sweat from her brow with her wrist, then gestured for me to pass. I always saw her from a distance peeking out from behind her laced curtains at our house. This was the first time I saw her up close. Her cheeks were a rosy red. She must even scrub them I thought as I hurried past.

Germans were different from us. Their skin was fair. Ours dark. Their food predictable, ours pronounced. Their eyes blue. Ours black as Italian olives. But there was another big cultural difference. Scrubbing!

Our house was kitty-corner from the Brittenfeld's. Their lawn resembled a putting green. Ours was tightly packed earth. It did nothing to enhance the neighborhood, but it was perfect for Bocce ball.

Every morning my grandmother would tell me to sweep it. Sweep the dirt off the dirt, that way the dirt won't be dirty she would explain in Italian. Yet another mystery I hoped to clear up some day.

There was one perfectly cultivated area in our yard. Our vegetable garden. Every evening you could find my father, nurturing the the garlic, onions, oregano, eggplant, basil and zucchini. Not forgetting the centerpiece of every Italian garden, the one thing every family could gather around for warmth. The almighty tomato!

He always tucked a sprig of basil behind his ear as he tended the garden. When his masculinity was questioned about this , my father would simply smile and explain in fractured English. Basil was of the feminine gender, it was perfectly natural for a man to be that close. He loved it that much.

There was a grape arbor near our alley. Some pretty foul tasting wine came from these vines. The first mouthful was always followed by the scream of "vinegar!" Then an off kilter smile of intoxication immediately followed. It became the source for hardy laughter and off-key singing when visiting relatives came to visit.

German neighbors out for an evening walk would stop and gawk at this unusual outburst of humanity.

We were different than our German neighbors. The question was, are our German neighbors sympathetic to the Germans in Europe?

Adolph Hitler had proclaimed that Germans were the chosen race, superior to all other races. It was a quiet preoccupation whispered about but rarely spoken of around the neighborhood.

As a small boy one thing was clear as I watched the somber news reels at the Liberty Theater. A stunned audience watched as eerie images of thousands of conquering German troops flickered across the screen. The sound of hundreds of thousands of boots Goose stepping in unison sent chills up my tiny spine.

PRIDE, PREJUDICE  & APPLE PIE.

As I was sweeping the dirt off our dirt one afternoon a small woman approached.
She wore a colorful print dress and silk stockings. Her hair was in a tidy bun and her cheeks were extra rosy. She carried something covered with a yellow dish towel.
It was Lydia Brittenfeldt ! I had never seen her without a scrub brush and a bucket of soap suds ! She was beautiful .

Lydia tentatively approached our back door then tapped softly . My mother smiled through the screen then opened the door. Lydia removed the yellow dish towel revealing a freshly baked apple pie. My mother, moved by the masterpiece, invited her in.

Lydia began to speak, but choked on her first word. Tears welled up in her eyes then she turned and ran towards home.
My mother followed.

I remember them in the middle of the street hugging. Lydia sobbing, my mother drying her eyes with the yellow dish towel.

I found out another cultural difference that evening. God can Germans bake pastries !

After the incredible apple pie was devoured,my mom told this story :
We came from very different places. Lydia said. We have different ways. I was convinced you were below us. After watching how hard you and your husband work, how you raise your children, how important family is to you...I'm so ashamed for ever thinking such a thing. "

From that day on they shopped together. Shared recipes together. Canned pickles, saukraut and tomatoes together. Even shared intimate feminine problems together.
It would be a friendship that would last a lifetime.

The melting pot was on the burner.

KRAUT HEADS & SPAGHETTI BENDERS.

Kritts Field was more than a landing strip for oversized flying grasshoppers. It was a training ground for manhood, a place where the older boys taught the younger boys the fundamentals of football, baseball and life itself. I was in the batters box, arms cocked, hands choked up, eyes glued to the ball just like Walt Dagget instructed.

The ball wobbled slowly thru the air, its loose cover flapped as it approached the plate. It was a sucker pitch ! I didn't bite, took my time, and stroked it smoothly towards the tall weeds in right field. At least a ground rule triple I thought as the ball bounced from sight into the weeds.

It's detached cover landed just in front of Eddie Conrad near first. As I rounded first base,Eddie picked up the ball cover then tagged me. "You're out!" he gloated.

"That's not the ball." I spit back.

"Says Spaulding" he said holding up the cover. "That means you're out you little thit !"

That did it! He was mocking me because I lisped. The "s" sound was clearly not in my vocabulary.

I reached up and grabbed Eddie by the neck."Most of the ball is still somewhere in the weeds you big thit." I yelled back. Eddie's light blond Aryan hair now framed his flaming beet red face.

"Who you calling a big thit, you little thit!" Eddie barked. "You, you big thit! I choked out from the headlock Eddie had on me.

The unwritten rule was this. When someone picked on someone smaller than him, there was always someone bigger than him to settle things fairly. And so, Eric Wagner stepped in and separated the lopsided scuffle. Now if Eric wasn't at the top of this pecking order I 'm not sure who was.

"You little dago !" Red faced Eddie continued.

"You big kraut head!" I countered.

Eric being a man of very little words gave a head nod at Eddie in the direction of his house. Eddie scurried for home. "That'll teach you, kraut head." I yelled at Eddie now half way home.

Suddenly a strange chill filled the summer air over Kritts field. Only the buzz of distant flying grasshoppers broke the uncomfortable silence. Eric's steel blue German eyes stared through me for what seemed like forever. His jaw muscle twitched tensely. After a long silent pause Eric whispered. "I'm a kraut head too."

I played my best possum routine, I didn't move, blink or breathe. Maybe he'll leave me for dead I hoped.

Then Eric added "If I ever hear you call someone a kraut head again you know what I'll do ?"

I stood paralyzed. After a long lingering pause, Eric answered his own question. "I'll tell your mother !"

"Don't do it Eric, please, please." I begged. " I promise I'll never say it again! ever,never..... Cross my heart !"

My mother was a nudge under five feet tall. She earned her reputation last fall when she broke up football games with a broom handle because it went one minute after dinner time. Eric had never forgotten.

Then he looked down and offered me a short rare smile. I could feel the strength in his hand as he patted my boney shoulder blades. Then he slowly walked away.

It was then I knew Eric would never harm me. Nor would anyone else. The smile he gave me was warm... but there was a sadness I saw in it. A silent preoccupation was now dogging the older boys in the neighborhood as well. War was now eminent. Germans would be fighting Germans.

While we naively trained at play lot games, Hitler was training his youth for war. Will we be next to meet on the battlefield ?

I wondered.

FLYING MONKEYS & BLITZING PANZERS.

Mrs. Kritt had just taken most of the neighborhood to see the movie to end all movies. The Wizard of Oz. When it ended the house lights came on to a theater filled with charged up kids bursting to relieve a long awaited tinkle. Mrs. Kritt chaperoned some of our group to the toilet with strict orders for the rest of us to stay seated. Rudy Polstin entertained us with his standup version of the cowardly lion.
"Put up your dukes, C'mon ! C'mon!!!" Rudy blurted. I should have gone with the group...I peed my pants laughing. Even Burt Lahr would have wet his lion costume at Rudy's amazing performance.

Then the house lights dimmed and the RKO Pathe News intro began. We all watched in silent horror as grainy black and white images flickered on the screen. German Stuka dive bombers screamed as they plummeted vertically downward. The Polish earth shook under impact of raining German bombs.

Foot soldiers and the obsolete Polish horse Cavalry were no match for the advancing state-of-the-art Panzer Tank Divisions. Corpses of Polish soldiers and horses lie twisted in grotesque shapes.

Like a hysterical mother hen, a horrified Mrs. Kritt hurriedly ushered us from the darkened theater.

The German victory was swift, decisive, devastating. We had just witnessed the real world .Things were slowly coming together. Could this be why old man Schmidke stared silently?

Mrs. Kritt did her best to cheer things up as she sang and sipped along to Americas now favorite refrain "We're off to see the Wizard." We skipped homeward past the smelly hissing gas plant as it belched toxic waste into our precious Ox Creek. I tried hard to be enthusiastic, but my mind raced forward towards adolescence. There were "the movies," then there was "the real world." Which was a kid to believe? Even Santa Claus was suspect now.

HEARTSTRINGS & HONEYSUCKLE

The evening air was as warm as bath water.
As we reached the rim of the ravine the swell of violins drifted up to meet us.
The band shell at the bottom formed a natural acoustical setting.

The brass section joined in beautiful harmony to the strains of "Begin the Beguine." This was my first experience hearing live music. That is with the exception of the off-key notes from my father's accordion. Even at age seven I felt enormous emotions stir inside me.

The smell of dime store perfume mingled with the smell from the honeysuckle bushes nearby.

We settled into an area where most of our neighbors were seated. Even in silhouette I could recognize everyone. Even old Mr. Schmidke with his ever present dangling cigarette was here. I felt secure.

The powerful baritone gave his melodramatic rendition of Cole Porters beautifully crafted lyrics.
"I'm with you once more under the stars. Down by the shore an orchestra's playing. It brings back the night of tropical splendor."
Was this a coincidence?
No it wasn't. Mr. Porter was defining this place. This night. It was like a movie...and we were in it !

As my eyes slowly became accustomed to the dim lighting I noticed some startling differences. I had never seen the neighborhood girls dressed up before. They were no longer little girls but beautiful young women. Their tight fitting fuzzy sweaters revealed some startling new developments. Nylon stockings now defined long shapely legs. The thin black seam line ran from the heel up the back of the leg to places I could only imagine.
Gulp, I thought.

Their ruby red lipstick enhanced their already perfect teeth. They whispered softly as they batted their store bought eye lashes flirtatiously toward the boys.

The boys seemed dazed and stupefied by all this. Definitely out of character.

They mumbled words like "necking" and "making out" as they giggled nervously at each other. I was sure, however, that when they whispered "getting to first base," they weren't talking about baseball.

The boys were being swept away by some unknown force, stronger then their own will. What bothered me most was that they were oblivious to my presence.
I was losing my mentors ! My heroes! To girls !

It took me years to realize what actually happened that night. The Discovery Channel helped. The female of the species clearly decides the pulse of life. The male willingly dances to it.

Only one question remaining was the mystery of the thin black seam up the nylon stockings.
That wasn't resolved until I was well into adolescence.

But that enchanted night remains.
When I'm on a crowded elevator, or in a dentist's chair and "Begin the Beguine" begins, I' m back there.
At the rim of that ravine, slipping slowly down into the bath water of that evening.

WHITE SATIN, DIAMONDS & PEARL.

We rushed past the long black limo and up the stairs of Our Lady of Pompeii church. The wedding ceremony was already in progress. We were ushered to the bride's section in the front row. Our city relatives, already seated, offered us a huge collective smile.

Phyllis waited a long time for a man like Carlo. He wasn't the prince charming most brides wish for, but he was most reliable. That's what really mattered insisted the neighborhood matriarchs. A shoemaker by trade would promise her a solid future. Shoes will always wear out. Carlo would always provide Phyllis financial security. But I think Carlo provided much more than they all realized. Whenever Carlo looked at Phyllis and twitched his pencil mustache , Phyllis' face turned a cherry red.

Young future bride hopefuls were at the edge of their seats. Waiting for that pinnacle moment, to hear Phyllis say the two most important words in her young life. "I do."

When the question came, low whispers from the church vestibule interrupted her answer. The interruptive murmurs grew louder and louder.

The ceremony stopped. Faces turned from curious to serious as the whispering spread up towards the altar. Finally, the message came.

"Japan had just attacked the United States. A major portion of our Pacific Feet had been destroyed." the Monsignor announced.

"Thousands of young American lives have been lost. Let us all pray in silence for the souls of our fellow Americans." the Monsignor added sadly.

An erie hush fell over the cavernous church. I felt my mothers arm cover me protectively. Something was more serious than my young mind could ever understand. I burrowed my face into her shoulder. The click of rosaries could be heard above the mumbling appeals to our Lady of Pompeii. The reality of war was now here.

An old veteran nearby starred glassy eyed. He was one of the few that knew the hardship and suffering we were about to face.

After the ceremony, a tear drained Phyllis stood at the top of the church stairs. Her bridesmaids tried to console her to no avail. The dream she had as a little girl was now a living nightmare. Would Carlo be swept away into this horrible war? she wondered.

Children now scurried at Phyllis's feet. Happily collecting little bags of candy-coated almonds and good luck pennies. All oblivious to her pain.

Two caged love birds perched high on top of the stately wedding cake. Every Italian delicacy from artichokes to ziti covered the long white table cloth.

Word was that Carlo had spared no expense for the wedding reception. There also was much speculation about how many shoes he would have to repair to cover this extravaganza.

Somewhere out in the Pacific Ocean, Japanese pilots raised their saki cups in jubilation. Meanwhile, in Chicago on Halsted Street, a spiritless band played to an empty dance floor.

Back at the Victory ritual, Admiral Yamamoto, Commander in-Chief of the Japanese Imperial Navy, watches the celebrating pilots in somber silence.

" I fear all we have done is to awaken a sleeping giant " he was quoted as telling his officers.

The tradition at the wedding " Bridal Table."was to toast the bride. More correctly it should be called the "Testosterone Table." A group of nervous young men gathered under a cloud of cigarette smoke to ponder their immediate future.

Joey Partapillo breaks the awkward silence.
" I don't know about you guys, but I'm not taking this sitting down!" he bellowed as he downs a Sambucca.
"Hey, easy, Joey, this is a wedding." someone offered.
"But they sucker punched us!" Joey replies.
Punctuated by another shot.
"That makes em' a bunch of yellow bellied bastards!"
Joey slurs on!
Followed by another Sambucca, and another.

" I fear all we have done is to awaken a sleeping giant."

Then, with head resting on his elbow Joey slurs out one final threat.
"I'll tell you one thing ! They're gonna hear it from Joey P !"

The Japanese Imperial fleet will be safe, at least for tonight. Joey is now sound asleep at the bar.

The train ride back home to Michigan was different that night. The sky was now a pulsing purple orange . Distant blast furnaces from the steel mills at Gary groaned and hissed in the distance. Like a fire breathing monster that had awakened from a peaceful slumber.

Was this what Admiral Yamamoto was talking about?

REMEMBRANCE & REDEMPTION.

"The only thing we have to fearaa is fearaa it self."

The orange light on our radio pulsed with every word. Franklin Delano Roosevelt , our benevolent president was addressing our nation. My father's massive hands lay gently folded in his lap like an obedient child, his ears absorbed every word.

FDR spoke with aristocratic eloquence. Words an unschooled Italian peasant would never understand. But it was the power in which they were spoken that gave my father all the comfort he needed.

At his Inaugural Address President Roosevelt proclaimed in his lofty "sing song" style said
"The only thing we have to fear, is fear itself."
It contained the perfect idea to gather around. "Fear" was a vital weapon our enemies would use on us.
Without fear, our mission would be clear.
We had been attacked. Innocence was now gone.
Only focused resolve remained.
America changed that night. It would be an America I would never see again in my lifetime.

RED, WHITE & THE BLUES.

I got a hollow feeling as I walked the neighborhood. Overnight, the boys were gone. Each replaced by a tiny flag baring a blue star in their honor. Each star signifying a boy off to fight the war. The Kraft flag had five stars.

Kritts field was strangely silent. I stared sadly at the empty baseball diamond. The footprints on the base paths were the only evidence that the boys were even here. "Not one goodbye!" I thought sadly, "That really hurts !"

A large hand tapped me on my shoulder from behind. I didn't recognize him for a moment . I had never seen Marv Ward without his perpetual jaunty grin. He paused for a moment then forced a small smile. "Take this" he said, softly. "It's yours now."

"I can't take this, Marv," I said. " It's a brand new football, I can still smell the leather."

"I won't be using it anymore." he replied.

My mind raced ! What did he mean by that ?

Did he mean he wouldn't make it back from the war ? Is this his way of saying goodbye forever ?

I was ready to throw up.

Marv must have read my pale white face.

"Don't worry. I'll be back when the war's over." he said confidently,"But I'll be a man, then I'll need a job, not a football."
I was relieved. I tucked the ball under my arm.

Then Marv got down on one knee, looked at me nose to nose and said,"Listen, you boys are the men now. It's up to you kids to take care of everything in the neighborhood while we're gone. Understand ?" I could feel my heart race at the thought of that responsibility.

"I'll take good care of it 'til you come home." I said with false confidence, tucking the football under my arm.
"Make sure to use it, Genie." he said, flashing that infectious smile. A full two rows of perfect white teeth appeared...then he waved.
I returned the smile.
The word "goodbye" was never spoken.

First Lieutenant Marvin Ward made it through the war unscathed.
The football was wounded in action.

One by one, the boys left our neighborhood. Overnight, the mood changed from idyllic to unsettling. So many questions lingered. Were our German boys ready to fight Germany? To fight or kill their own blood relatives? Then there were the Japanese Americans. A silent undercurrent about mistrust of their loyalty quietly circulated , but little was ever said. The battle lines on the home front were unclear.

Many German boys were assigned to Army Intelligence in the European Theater of war. Speaking fluent German, they would be very valuable dealing with our our enemies.

The Japanese Culture was a mystery to the Western Culture. This caused great pain for the Japanese Americans. Many were impounded and held until the war ended. At age eleven, there was no way to understand the mind boggling politics of it all.

"We have nothing to fear but fear itself" were the words President Roosevelt so eloquently stated. Yes, the war was oceans away, but there was little discussion that the San Francisco skyline could be viewed by Japanese periscopes and that Lady Liberty showed clearly in German cross hairs.

Each week, carefully crafted radio reports stated "Two medium Allied ships were sunk this week." Those were the words we lived by. The reality was quite different. The real count averaged thirty-three each week. Thirty one sunken freighters were simply ignored. I can't remember any panic. In fact, some people on the eastern seaboard got so comfortable they planned beach outings to watch the fireworks.

Later on, captured German films revealed German submariners taking in a Yankee baseball game after a hard weeks work sinking Allied ships.

Because of the covert action many of the Merchant Marine records were hidden. A staggering 8,000 American boys were known to have gone down with their ships. That's more American fatalities than in the infamous Normandy Invasion.

Winston Churchill openly admitted that enemy submarines were his single worst fear.
Yet, our home front remained fearless and focused.

What we didn't know didn't hurt us.

MITSUBISHIS & MESSERSCHMITTS.

The war was now raging on all fronts. Back home, the snow fell silently on Kritts field. Tiny boys bundled in leggings and ear muffs huddled near the snow covered pitchers mound. Only the squeak of rubber galoshes could be heard as they shuffled nervously on the frozen turf. The somber reality of war was sinking in. Not the war games we played complete with lunch breaks, the bullets were real.

"What can we do to help ?" I asked the group.
" We're only kids."
" First you can wipe your runny nose" Rudy Polstin giggled. The comic relief was most welcome.
Even I laughed.

Donnie began: "As of now old man Becker is our neighborhood air raid warden. He makes sure all lights are out during air raid drills, but his chronic back problem limits his field of vision to hunting for night crawlers. Unfortunately, the sky is in the opposite direction."
"We have to give the old geezer a hand right?" I offered.
"No, an eye." Donnie answered (pause) "and a little respect for old Mr. Becker."

Then Donnie looked up and pointed to the crisp cobalt sky.
We all stood gawking. Even Gerry Ellis wiped his foggy glasses then squinted skyward.

" If the enemy comes, they'll come from there first." We soaked up every word. Only Gerry Ellis , his glasses steamed up as usual, seemed oblivious to Donnie's concerns. I couldn't help but agree with Gerry Ellis. It would have to be one confused saki soaked Japanese pilot to show up over Kritts Field

Don was relentless." We have to keep our eyes on the sky." He kept repeating.

Somehow the words felt heroic. Each punctuated by Donnie's warm breathe as it wafted into the cold air. As if frozen in time. "Our first meeting will be in Bill Kritts basement tomorrow at O eight hundred hours. That's 8 A.M. civilian time." He added. Then we all headed our separate ways.

I stood on the pitchers mound, my imagination still churning as I scanned the blank winter sky. Did Donnie know something we didn't ? The sound of my racing

heart brought me back to earth. Yes, it could happen. I scanned the blank winter sky, carefully scrutinizing each direction. Then with a sigh of relief, I headed home.

The welcome smells of dinner met me as I opened our back door. " Close the door you're letting the heat out. " my mother barked as she stirred the sauce. "Take off those wet boots and...good God! what's that awful smell ?"

"Jeez! Ugh! Phew ! Whitey Polstin, the beer drinking German Shepherd did it again !"

In my eagerness to "keep my eyes on the skies" I forgot to look down. I stepped into a fresh deposit Whitey left on the pitchers mound.

HEARTBREAK & HAVOC.

Mrs. Brownstein wore her hair in a loosely tied bun. Gray strands constantly unraveled around her face. She always greeted me with great exuberance. Her eye glass correction magnified her large hazel eyes. She was so short she even had to look up to a small boy like me.

"Look at you!" she would say in her thick Yiddish accent. " How beautifully you are !" She'd squeeze my face with her tiny hands and marvel at how much I'd grown since yesterday, then her hugely exaggerated eyes would well up with tears.

I was not a beautiful child by any means, but I soaked up every word.

But why the tears ? Were they simply tears of appreciation for the miracle of youth ?
Or were they a sad reminder of her own sons eyes.
It was only yesterday that Julius was a boy like me. Now he's shipping out to fight a war .

In the South Pacific the Japanese Navy methodically devoured every island in their wake. Back home Ensign Julius Brownstein was saying goodbye to the streets he grew up on. I watched from across the street as he walked by. His all white Naval Officers uniform, black epaulets and gold braid were a startling contrast to our scruffy neighborhood. His walk was steady, solemn, almost dutiful. He carried his emotions confidently aside,

His keen eyes were now focused on the new business at hand. His flying skills and his classic Jewish nose had earned him the nickname "Hawk" in flight school. He was now eager to prove it to the Imperial Japanese Navy.

Julius would pilot a Grumman F4F "Wildcat." This was no small task.

Of all the things he was about to face, saying "goodbye" to his bewildered parents had to be the hardest. I watched from behind a large maple tree as Julius gathered his tiny parents against him in one big hug. As if he were the parent, they now the children. It was hard to watch. I walked away.

Mr. and Mrs. Brownstein lived in a three story walk up apartment. Every evening you could see her unmistakable silhouette in the attic window. She picked the highest window to say her evening prayers. That way God would not miss one word, her grandson Billy Kritt explained.

There were other nights when the window was wide opened. An angry Mrs. Brownstein would shake her fist out the window towards the heavens. I didn't understand a word of Hebrew but her message was loud and clear to me.

I'm sure God forgave her outburst.
After all, her devotion goes back for an entire lifetime.

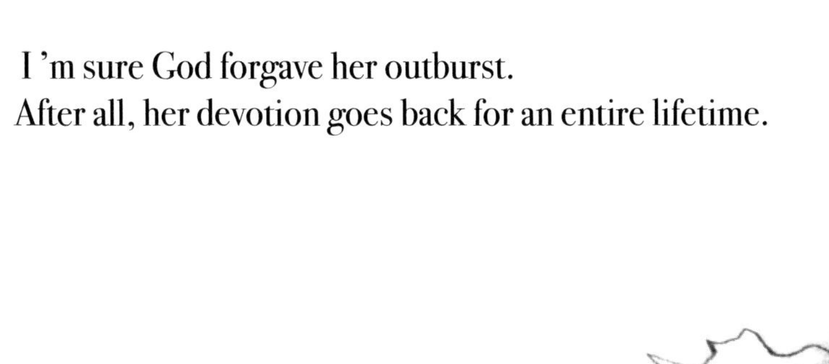

MITSUBISHIS & MESSERSCHMITTS.

It was a scene from a black and white war movie as Donnie began.

He explained the purpose of the club, why it was important to know and identify all aircraft, friend or foe.

Then he revealed an extensive stack of cards. Each card revealed a different aircraft with top and side view silhouettes of each aircraft. Painstakingly, he explained in detail how to separate allied from enemy aircraft.
The drill was to identify each in the flash of a card.
That included a complete breakdown of armament, air speed and horsepower, including the manufacturer names.

Donnie was deadly serious.
Gerry Ellis fell fast asleep.

Now, Gerry was not a typical kid. Definitely a dreamer. But was his lack of attention a clear act that the club was second priority to a good day dream. Whatever the case, Gerry was expelled from the club.

Gerry tried everything to convince Donnie otherwise. Finally, in desparation, Donnie offered one stipulation. If Gerry could spell "manufacturing" he might reconsider.

Remember now, this was 60 years before "spell check." Back when teachers gritted their teeth and said sternly " If you can't spell it, look it up in the dictionary!" "How can I look it up if I don't know how to spell it ?" was not an acceptable reply. Nevertheless, the next meeting Gerry was in the front row. My guess is he was the only one who could spell "manufacturing."

Our heavy bombers were taking their toll on enemy factories and our neighborhood boys were becoming bigger than life heroes.

Jaunty Ovie Menschinger manned a B-24 Liberator bomber. Having to fly through a pre arranged field of flack every mission, the crew was issued steel helmets. Ovie opted to sit on his rather than wear it.
"What's the use of living if you lose your manhood ?" Ovie figured.

Junior Schmiggle was a tail gunner on a B-17 "Flying Fortress." A seat reserved for only the smallest gunners. Out on a limb for all to see, they were the target German fighter pilots most cherished.

Eric Wagner was a side gunner on a B-17 "Flying Fortress" that bombed Germany over twenty times. He survived the flack barrages and Messerschmidt bullets.

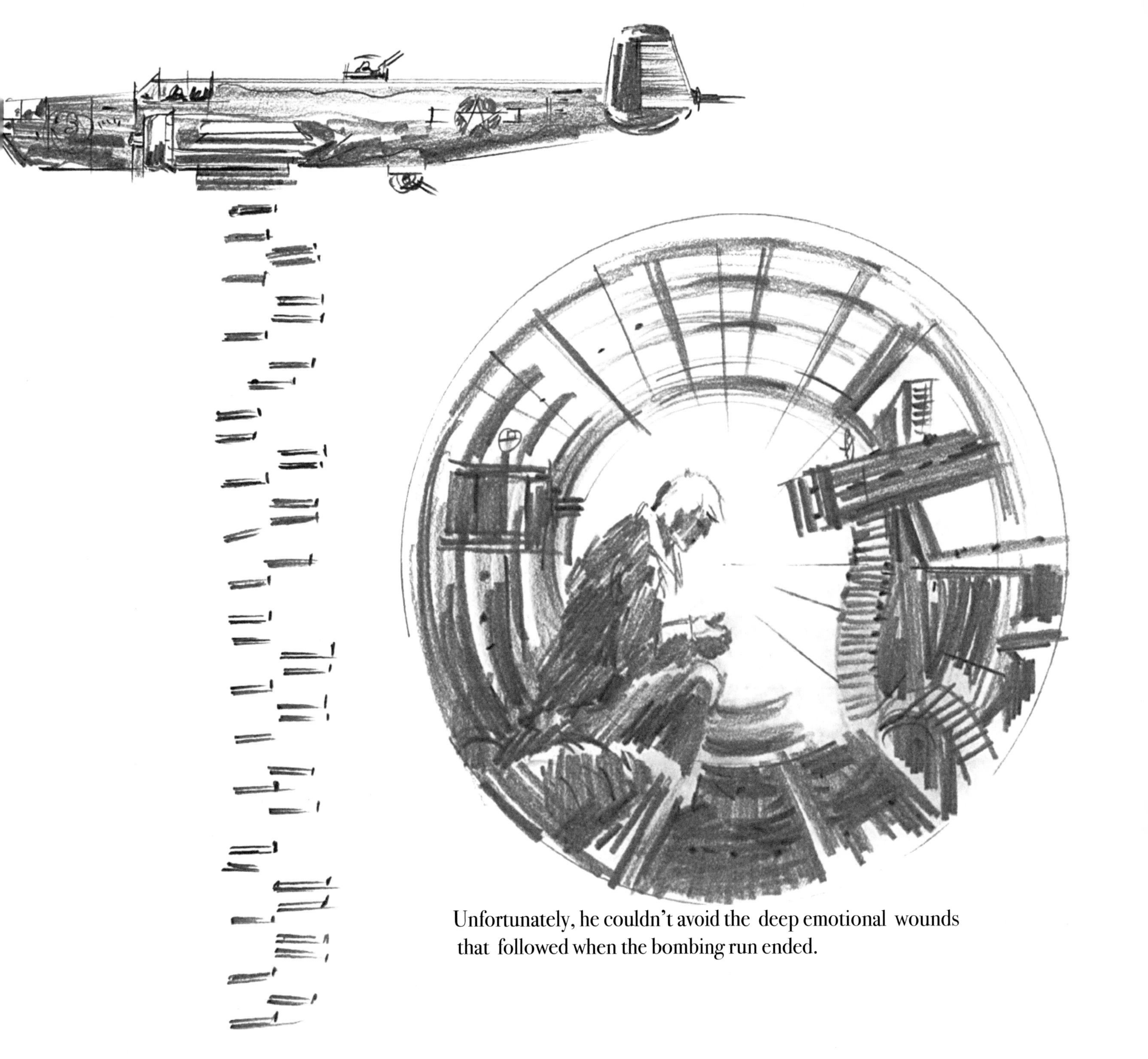

Unfortunately, he couldn't avoid the deep emotional wounds that followed when the bombing run ended.

SNIPS, SNAILS & ENTRAILS.

My mother gazed intently at the pathetic cut of meat. Mr. Schwartz grimaced as he tried to explain it's origin. The shriveled piece of meat was the only one available. All the choice cuts of meats were now rationed. To feed our troops that were off to fight the war.

The word "Parboiled'"was mentioned several times during the painful conversation. I found out later that par-boiling was a way to make even a leather shoe edible.

My mother grudging reached into her change purse, then a tug of war began. One hand trying to remove the dollar bill, the other desperately holding on.

When the transaction ended, Mr. Schwartz handed my mother a large bag filled with neck bones. Free of charge. Her face lit up. Neck bones are the magic that creates the best spaghetti sauce, and the price was right.

While she was still glowing over the free neck bones, I seized the opportunity to coax her into buying me bubble gum. "No butter! No sugar! No bubble gum! All off to the Var." Mr. Schwartz said sadly in his thick Yiddish accent.

Finally, the war really hit where it hurt. No bubble gum! Why would they need bubble gum to fight a war? This was the lowest of all blows. No pun intended.

On the way home we passed Mr. Schwanke washing his already spotless car. "No gasoline, no oil, no rubber!" he blurted, practically in tears. My mother faked a nod of sympathy as we walked past. Four blocks later as she trudged up our back stairs, her true feelings came out. "He treats that car better than his own wife! Let him walk like the rest of us!"

Having to ration didn't effect us much. Red meat rarely ever made it to our table. My mother cooked from the Italian peasant cook book. Meat was used only sparingly for flavoring . We ate the parts that were left over like the brains, kidneys and the stomach lining. On occasion, pickled pig ears and knuckles.

Chicken soup included the head, neck, and feet (complete with toe nails.) My father always grabbed the swollen purple chicken head. It's squinting eyes gave the impression that the chicken knew what was about to happen.

Then my father would would ceremoniously display it for all to see. We'd all squeal with delight as he ate it as if he was eating corn off the cob!

Once, my brother joined the fun, picked up a chicken foot and pointed all four toe nails at me.

I took the other foot and we began dueling like two fighting roosters. We were charged with "playing with our food," then punished on the spot.

Bare legs were becoming the patriotic fashion. Silk and nylon were desperately needed to make parachutes.
Women sacrificed one of their many alluring charms for the war effort. I can't even imagine how many pairs of nylons it took to make just one parachute.
I'm sure many paratroopers mused lustfully over that question on their decent to earth.

VICTORY ON LAND, SEA & IN THE GARDEN.

I awoke to the sound of distant church bells. I could smell the garlic from the kitchen as it simmered in hot olive oil. Must be Sunday I thought as I turned over to find a more comfortable sleeping position.

I felt my brothers foot as he placed it firmly against my chest. Then with a push, pinned me against the wall. He was not a morning person.

As I settled into a comfortable ball, the covers flew off the bed. With a shriek my mother announced "This is the last time I'm gonna tell you! Get your little butt's going !"

"I'm going to get the broom , and when I get back, you both better be gone!" She bellowed as she headed for the broom closet.

We scrambled into our white uniforms left over from our first Holy Communion a few Sunday's ago.

As I fumbled to tie my tie, my brother began to unbutton my shirt. "This shirt is mine." he growled.

"It's mine." I answered. " See, it fits me perfect."

"No, this is yours." he said firmly as he held up a wrinkled shirt splattered with orange spaghetti stains.

"Ouch, it's even got my fingerprints all over it." I thought as I reluctantly surrendered the clean shirt.

My mother burst into the room with a broom. Each swing was punctuated by a four letter word.

Now don't misunderstand. My mother went to church every day, religiously. Prayed the Holy Rosary every night, religiously, and swore in two languages, religiously.

We split up. My mother chased my brother out the front, I ran out the back towards the garden.

My father was there as usual, watering the garden. As I tried to run past him, he turned and grabbed me by my flapping shirt tail.

"Where are you going, Genie?" He asked in Italian.

"I gotta go to church!" I blurted.

He look at me with some puzzlement, smiled, then said. "Aww, that'sa bullashit !

"Ouch ! That's blasphemy!" I thought. Even to mention Holy Mother church and bullshit in the same sentence would get you purgatory if you were lucky.

"Hail Mary full of grace." I prayed. "The Lord is with...with...with, thee... Blessed art thou among women... and...and... please forgive my father. He's just an ignorant immigrant. He really means well...he's..."

"You wana see God ?" My father interrupted.

Now he wants to show me God! I panicked.

"Dear God, please don't strike him down." I begged.

My father took my hand, smiled, then led me to an empty fruit crate in the middle of the garden. My heart was in my throat.

"Sit here." he said calmly in Italian.

I sat down on the orange crate placed under me. My eyes were tightly closed, waiting for the lightning bolt to strike..

"See? It'sa God." he whispered in my ear.

I slowly opened my eyes.

A giant beefsteak tomato blocked my view.

Then he gently cupped the tomato in his hugh hand, smiled and said.
"Yesterday she was alla green. Today she's alla red!"
Then his eyes widened and he said.
"See.Thats'a God!"
I stared at the beefsteak tomato.The soft red fusion into the green gave the appearance that the tomato was ripening before my eyes!
Truly, it was a phenomenon I had over looked.

Then he pointed to the zucchini and said. "Look, yesterday she was a small flower." He lifted the large zucchini leaf with his work boot revealing a zucchini perfect for picking.
"Thats'a God."
'You no have to go to church to be witha God.
He'sa right here. In our garden." He declared proudly.

Out of the corner of my eye I saw my mother and her broom. Like a Buckingham Palace guard at parade rest, she looked through me as if I were invisible.
I was truly moved at what I just saw, but my better judgment said. "Igottagotochurch !!!"

The smell of incense moved me. The Latin chant from the choir swept me away, but my thoughts kept going back to that tomato. In the garden.

Franklin Roosevelt, our beloved President, strongly urged all Americans to grow gardens. That gardens were vital to the war effort. So vital in fact, that they be called "Victory Gardens."
He must have known the tomato story.

One Saturday morning Donnie called an emergency meeting. An imposing package from The United States Naval Department had just arrived. It was addressed to our airplane spotters club.
Gulp! Even the mail carrier was impressed.
The returned address read: Ensign Julius Brownstein , undisclosed, South Pacific.

A tiny sweat mustache appeared under Donnie's nose as he nervously opened the package.
Yikes! It contained Five 8"x10" A P wire photos along with an onion paper note from "Hawk" himself !

They were photos of an aborted take off caused by extremely high seas. In sequence, they showed Juicy's Grumman Wildcat drop from the deck into the turbulent water. Then the cockpit slid open as Juicy's plane sank beneath him. Then Donnie revealed the last photo. The Wildcat had disappeared from sight under the angry turbulent waters ..... but Juicy was still afloat!
A hugh collective cheer went up bringing a panicked Mrs. Kritt down to the basement.

It's reported that sometimes, even in high seas, takeoffs are necessary. The abort ratio can be as high as two planes out of five. The consequence just as deadly as Japanese anti-air craft fire.

AIRMAIL FOR ADOLPH.

My older brother Vince was deep in thought at the breakfast table. I was half asleep as I fumbled around the kitchen for a clean coffee cup.

I poured myself a cup of coffee, added a generous amount of milk, two tablespoons of sugar and three saltine crackers .This ritual was the source of much criticism. Nevertheless, it continued to be my breakfast of choice all the way through high school.

As I watched the last cracker sink from sight, I whispered. " The Grumman Wildcat is sinking... it's going...going...It's gone!"

"You're hopeless." Vince mumbled. "Everything's a war game to you. Juicy could have died you know. Now eat that cup of mush you call breakfast and get dressed. Remember? We're going alley junking!"

I gulped down my breakfast. God, did I love alley junking.

First stop was the Brown family. They owned the Brown Ice & Coal Company. We couldn't survive a winter without their coal or a summer without their ice. They owned the town. Their trash was magnificent!

I dug furiously into the trash like an alley cat digging for a rat ! " Look at this." I said as I put a white Palm Beach hat on my head. "And these." holding up a pair of brand new wing-tipped Oxfords still in shoe trees.

"We're trying to fight a war." Junior answered impatiently as he dug deeply into the trash. "Something like this." he explained, holding up a clothes iron.

I didn't get the concept. "Look!" he snapped, putting the iron in my hand.

" They melt this metal down then make a bomb out of it." "Ouch!" I said. "This could really hurt ...especially if you dropped it from an airplane."

The concept finally sunk in..

"Hey Junior, I know where something really big is. It's really heavy...and it's only a short walk from here." I

offered enthusiastically, as I headed for Conkeys Field. Vince reluctantly followed.

Conkeys Field stretched out for at least six city blocks in all directions. Big enough in fact to comfortably fit Ringling Brothers entire Circus, including all the elephants, lions, tigers and still have room for the fat lady !

We headed into the tall grass where the road ended near the ravine. The summer growth had camouflaged it completely. I had spotted this strange configuration last winter buried under a foot of snow. I knew exactly where it was. I could see dollar signs in my brother's eyes as he struggled to dislodge it from its resting place.

Using ancient Egyptian leverage, he had it on the wagon in a heart beat.

"What is it ?" I asked.

"Money." He replied in his lowest voice.

As I look back, it must have been a piece of machinery left behind from the Ringling Brothers Circus.

Most importantly, it was desperately needed for the war effort. Metal, copper and rubber were most needed to fight the war.

We were up before first light the next morning. My brother never bothered to explain why the ungodly hour. I knew him well enough never to ask.

We headed for the salvage yards in an area nick named "The Flats." The wagon groaned under the weight of our treasure. Fortunately, it was all down hill, which worked to our advantage until the last twenty yards when we had to let go, letting the wagon choose its own course. The wagon announced its own arrival in front off Mr. Sax's yard.

Three salvage yards sat all in a row. Each Jewish owned and operated. All combined they constituted 2,000 years of moxie negotiating skills.

Any average kid off the street could be in trouble against this savvy competition, but my brother was no average off the street kid. Carefully he played Mr. Sax against Mr. Jacobsen against Mr. Zimmerman.
They were no match my street wise brother.
Even when folding money was waved under his nose he was unflappable.
"Take it Junior, take it." I whispered.
He put his index finger to his mouth, looked me directly in the eyes, then clamped both rows of teeth down on it.
Sicilian Translation: Shut up or your ass is grass..... and I'm a lawnmower.
I got the message. Mr. Zimmerman got the message.
Even Mr. Sax got the message. This is a tough customer.
" Lets go,Genie." he said as he turned the wagon to leave.
"O.K. Ten dollars !" Mr.Sax snapped.
"and two hot fudge sundaes !" my brother added...
"and two hot fudge sundaes." Mr. Sax surrendered.
The wagon groaned to a halt.

As we sat at the marble counter eating our hot fudge sundaes my brother explained something not many gentiles know. There's an ancient Hebrew superstition that if you lose your first customer it will be a bad business luck all day. Mr. Sax was at our mercy.

We were the first customers on salvage row that morning. That explained the ungodly wake up call.

I felt my brothers' eyes looking at me. He held back his smile, but his eyes were dancing.

"What?" I asked as I inhaled a spoonful of ice cream. In an unprecedented gesture of affection, he patted me gently on my back.

I never said a word to Junior, but I saw something in Mr. Sax's face he may have missed. Thinking back about what was happening to European Jews, nobody more than Mr. Sax wanted that huge hunk of iron to be the bomb that dropped on Adolph Hitler′s head.

I would have held out for twenty dollars

LUST, LOVE & WAR.

While the endless rattle of Japanese machine guns echoed through the South Pacific, strains of "Lady of Spain" shrieked through the neighborhood. Germans, out for an evening stroll gawked as Albert took center stage in our backyard.
Rumor was he played the accordion professionally in Chicago. Wow!

Albert was exempt from duty in the military, which made him a highly eligible bachelor. He wore tiny round glasses with thick lenses that resembled two Coca Cola bottle bottoms.

His pupils were tiny black pinholes because of the severe eye correction. This was clearly the reason for his 4F draft status in the military.

He sat spread eagle to accommodate his large accordion, exposing a small sack that resembled a garlic bulb with three cloves, which was evident to everyone including my older sister Theresa.

My father, a wanna be musician, was swept away by Alberts' performance. His parents would look adoringly at him then at my older sister Theresa for her response.
Theresa, barely legal, would sit with her knees tightly together trying to force a smile of approval.

Her hair was still in long black Shirley Temple curls. My brother and I, knowing that Albert was on the approved list of suitors, stared at the strange garlic sack, then back at Theresa and giggle. This would be something we'd pay for dearly.

The following Monday our guests left for Chicago. A relieved Theresa sat in the kitchen, humming as she snapped green beans for our evening dinner. My brother and I were in our bedroom next to the kitchen.

"Pssst ! Genie, I'll be the accordion and you sing." Vince whispered. I nodded affirmative.

His introduction sounded surprisingly like Albert's accordion. I knew my queue and began to sing "Lady of Spain I adorrrrrrre you... Right from the first time I saaaaaw you."

A broom handle entered the room followed by Theresa. We ducked under the first roundhouse swings then headed out the kitchen door. I taunted Theresa with a smirk as I headed out the back door after Vince.

I remember the smell of peroxide. Then the sound of Theresa crying hysterically, screaming my name, trying to revive me over the blood filled kitchen sink. I had run into the door Vince had closed behind him. The gash on my forehead joined another I got the week before from a baseball bat. Together they formed a perfect "V" on my forehead.

"V for Victory." people would tell me "How patriotic."

Theresa had other suitors, but only one love. Back in grammar school when the word "dago" was even whispered in Theresa's presence, young Jack Palmer would appear from nowhere to snuff out any word that followed.

Jack grew up to become a perfect physical specimen. Easily, the most athletic boy in the neighborhood, regardless of sport. He was a man of few words, but every word counted.

Life didn't come easy for him. He grew up with eight sisters. All charmers. All ballbusters. This may have been one of the reasons Jack's father left for parts unknown, leaving Jack to drop out of high school to fill in the financial void.

The uncertainty of war definitely hurried the courting process. Jack was drafted, engaged and married Theresa within the year. After six weeks of Infantry boot camp, Theresa joined him in Ft. Lewis,Washington. A few months later Jack was shipped to Europe with two grotesque options. To kill or be killed. That was the way things were.

I still remember Theresa, now a young mother, kissing Jack goodbye. There was a desperation about it I'd never seen before. I couldn't help but fear the worst. Would this be their last kiss ?

The last news we heard from lustful Albert was, he was living happily in Chicago with his main squeeze.
His accordion.

ROSIE THE WIFE, MOTHER & THE RIVETER.

At age fifteen young Rosie was told that she would marry Vincenzo Mandarino.
It was an arrangement she tolerated but not without protest.
On occasion, to keep the record straight, she would announce "I don't love your father."
"Please, mama," we begged, "say you love him."
"It was my duty to marry him." she said firmly. "That's the way things were."
"Make no mistake." she added. " I respect your father greatly." As a consequence the word "love" was never spoken around our house.
The word "respect "quietly took it's place.

"Love" was a worn out word heard at movies. A word so over used it had no real meaning.
"Respect" on the other hand was a word real people could rely on.

Rosie dutifully took her place as mother, wife, maid, cook and accountant of paltry funds that barely trickled into our house.
Vincenzo was a railroad worker. Slave labor by today's standards, but a welcome option to starvation.
He looked like Douglas Fairbanks Jr. in work clothes. If you could visualize that.
A leading man charmer that handed over his heart every time he laid eyes on Rosie.

Each evening after setting a perfect dinner table, she'd scurry to freshen up before his arrival. "Are we having company?" I'd ask, as she powdered her freshly washed face. " No." she'd answer blotting her lipstick. " Then why did you put rouge on, mama ?" I'd ask hopefully.
"Just go meet your father." She'd snap impatiently.

My brother and I would race to meet him. He'd gather us effortlessly into his powerful arms. I'd bury my face into his massive chest. He smelled of burnt steel rail filings, tie soaked creasode and layers of weekly sweat. We held on like two small monkeys as he broke into a run pretending to shake us off. God what a thrill that two hundred yard ride was.

He would always inhale deeply when he entered the kitchen. Hold his breath, then look at Rosie and smile. She would blush then faked a struggle as he nuzzled his mustache into her soft neck. She'd giggle like a school girl as she fumbled to catch a loose earring. Then give him that "Not in front of the children look"and gently push him away.

Vincenzo always shaved before dinner. My mother never joined us at the dinner table. She'd stand by like a fussy waiter making sure every thing was in place.

I was a “chronic spiller.” No one wanted to sit next to me. When everyone was finally seated the ritual would begin. Vincenzo would fold his giant hands in prayer, smile then look up at our kitchen ceiling. Our own Sistine Chapel, I thought, as I looked up at the network of plaster cracks above.
“Jesusa Christ!” He began in broken English. “ This isa beautiful.”
We peeked over our clasped hands, struggling to hold back laughter.
Was he addressing Jesus Christ ? or was he using his name as an expletive of how good the food looked ?
Loosely translated that’s cussing.
Then we’d break down in uncontrolled laughter.

The silverware would leap up as his giant fist came down on the table.
“Silenco! Jesusa Christ!” he’d growl .
“Can’t you see Ima talka to God?”
Maybe God doesn’t understand pidgin English, but I clearly heard swearing that time. Then he’d look back up at the ceiling, smile and continue.
“This isa beautiful!” he said as his fork speared a zucchini slice, critiquing the meal as he prayed. “Homemade bread.”he mumbled as he buried his nose into a piece of still steaming bread.

He spoke as though God was actually here in our humble kitchen. As if they were long time friends sharing his thoughts as he sampled each delightful taste.

I could hardly imagine the starvation that forced him to leave his beloved Italy.
"We're so lucky." he said. "Common kids!....eat! eat !"
From the adjoining room Rosie couldn't hold back her smile. I'm sure she was wondering, how could you not love a man so kind as Vincenzo ?

Vincenzo was a lucky man. He had everything a man could want, but the war was about to change all that. Men were heading for the battlefield. Women were desperately needed at the defense plants. Rosie's life was about to change. For the better.
The independence she always longed for was now in front of her.

Barely five foot high, born in Italy and only a grammar school graduate, she spoke with the disposition of a trial lawyer, in flawless English.
She'd be a perfect fit in the boardroom but settled for the assembly line.

Rosie took the night shift at the defense plant. Four-thirty to midnight. The quality of suppertime was about to take a power dive.

Sometimes my brother and I would peek through the factory window and watch her work There was a vibrant glow about her I'd never seen before.
Finally, Rosie was living her dream.

Back home we all gathered silently around a catchall pot we reluctantly called "dinner." I remember my father starring vacantly at the meager table setting, his hands clasped together, over his face. He glanced up at the ceiling, then back at the pot, then up at the cracked ceiling and began.
"Jesusa Christ!" (A long pause)
"I worka myass off !" There was a long dead silence. Then he added. "I busta myballs !"
Did I hear right ? Ouch, this could get serious !

Then, fishing around in the pot, his fork emerges with a dangling piece of chicken . "Chicken froma Tuesday!" He announced. " Necka bone's froma Sunday!"

We sat frozen in place and watched as he flipped his fork aside. That did it, he pressed his friendship way past the limit!
I closed my eyes and waited for the ceiling to fall on us. This will definitely be our last supper!

Arms still folded in defiance he surveys our horrified faces...then a light bulb goes on. It dawns on him that he's talking to Almighty God himself!

The backpedaling begins. Sheepishly, he looks up at the ceiling and his most charming smile emerges.

Biting into a piece of stale bread he fakes his best compliment."Ummm.The bread from lasta week... Its stilla agood ! Looka spinach ! I lovea spinach !"
He actually eats a forkful to prove he's sincere.

Then smiling, spinach trailing from his lip, he realizes that this warm pot of whatever is quite good.

Then with head bowed in humble resignation he whispers. "Thanka you dear God."

My father never hid his true feelings while talking to God. His reason was simple "God already knows how I feel." he would say.

One afternoon my sister Theresa and my mother were having coffee. Having married so young in life, there was very few years between them. At times they were like sisters. There was a long pause in the conversation as Theresa stared directly into Rosie's eyes. My mother stared back directly into Theresa's eyes then ordered "If you have something to say, just say it."

Theresa calmly sipped her coffee then asked.
"You always said you never loved daddy.
Is that true ?"
"Thats true" my mother answered confidently.
"Then why did you get pregnant and have all us kids ?" Theresa replied.
I think I'll go play with my cat Nelly, I thought as I scurried out the door.
My mother was speechless.
Then in a soft voice she answered.
"I'm only human."

There was a long pause.
Then they both broke down and giggled like two giddy teenagers.

I'm not sure if Rosie was actually a riveter or not. "Classified info" she would always answer. "Let those bastards find out the hard way." She always added.

My mother never minced her words. In fact the only thing she ever minced was garlic.

One thing was clear.
The woman working force made a remarkable impact in the war.

A German officer said it best : "One German Tiger Tank is superior to four American made Sherman Tanks. The problem is, the Americans always show up with five."

WILDCATS, HELLCATS & FLYING GRASSHOPPERS

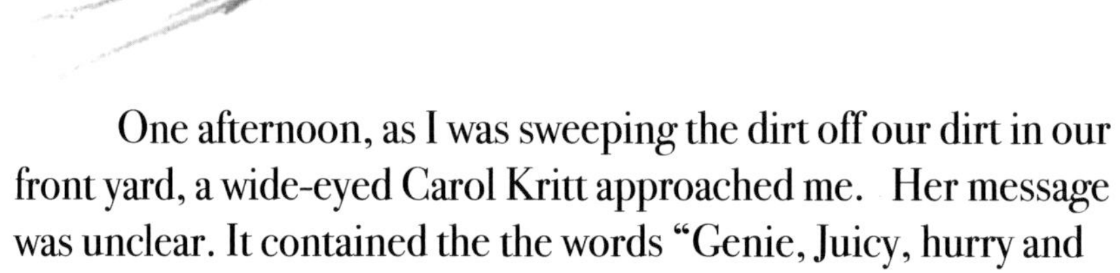

One afternoon, as I was sweeping the dirt off our dirt in our front yard, a wide-eyed Carol Kritt approached me. Her message was unclear. It contained the the words "Genie, Juicy, hurry and Kritts Field." Not necessarily in that order.

The last time I heard the word"Juicy" it was regarding Lt. Julius Brownstein and his squadron in the Pacific Ocean. Littering the Ocean bottom with Japanese submarine parts.

Most of the kids in the neighborhood were already in Kritts Field. Even Whitey, the beer drinking dog sensed that something was in the air. I couldn't help but notice that Donnie Richmond's feet shuffled nervously. As if he knew something we didn't.

It wasn't clear as to what was happening, but I knew it would be more exciting than sweeping dirt off dirt.

The anticipation was overwhelming. Jerry Ellis remained predictably stoic.

There was a strange silence. Only the familiar buzz of flying grasshoppers coming from the tall weeds in distant right field could be heard. Whitey began to whimper, then his ears snapped to attention. Now I heard it too. An unfamiliar drone had just joined the buzzing grasshoppers. We all looked at each other wide-eyed as the distant drone bellowed into dominance !

"There it is ! Just above Brown's barn !" usually stoic Jerry Ellis yelled as the giant war plane screamed overhead then quickly

disappeared from sight over the swaying maple trees that shaded home plate. We looked at each other in disbelief as a few dandelion seeds drifted past us.

We could hear the deep husky roar in the distance well below our view as it began to circle clockwise in the distance.

Then at treetop level it burst into view again ! We all screeched jumping up and down like popcorn popping on a hot stove.

"A Grumman F4F Wildcat !" someone yelled.
"Six 50 caliber machine guns." another added !
"50 Millimeter !" Donnie corrected. Then the plane banked for another pass. It was now clear. There was a large white American star framed by slate gray on top and creamy white on the fuselage below. Painted to blend in perfectly with the Pacific Ocean landscape. Whitey, now sober, barked with delight, his fur swaying back and forth with the second prop blast.

As the plane made its final pass something unearthly happened. The engine's roar vanished. The kids screams were now silent, even Whitey's barks were now muted.

I can't remember the plane moving. I could count each rivet now, even smell the exhaust fumes as the cockpit slowly slid open in slow motion. Then there it was. That unmistakable hawk nose.
"It's him ! It's him ! It's "Juicy"! We all screamed and waved. His wave was in slow motion and still lingers when I think of it today.
Time stopped that day.

Then like it never happened.....the sky was empty.

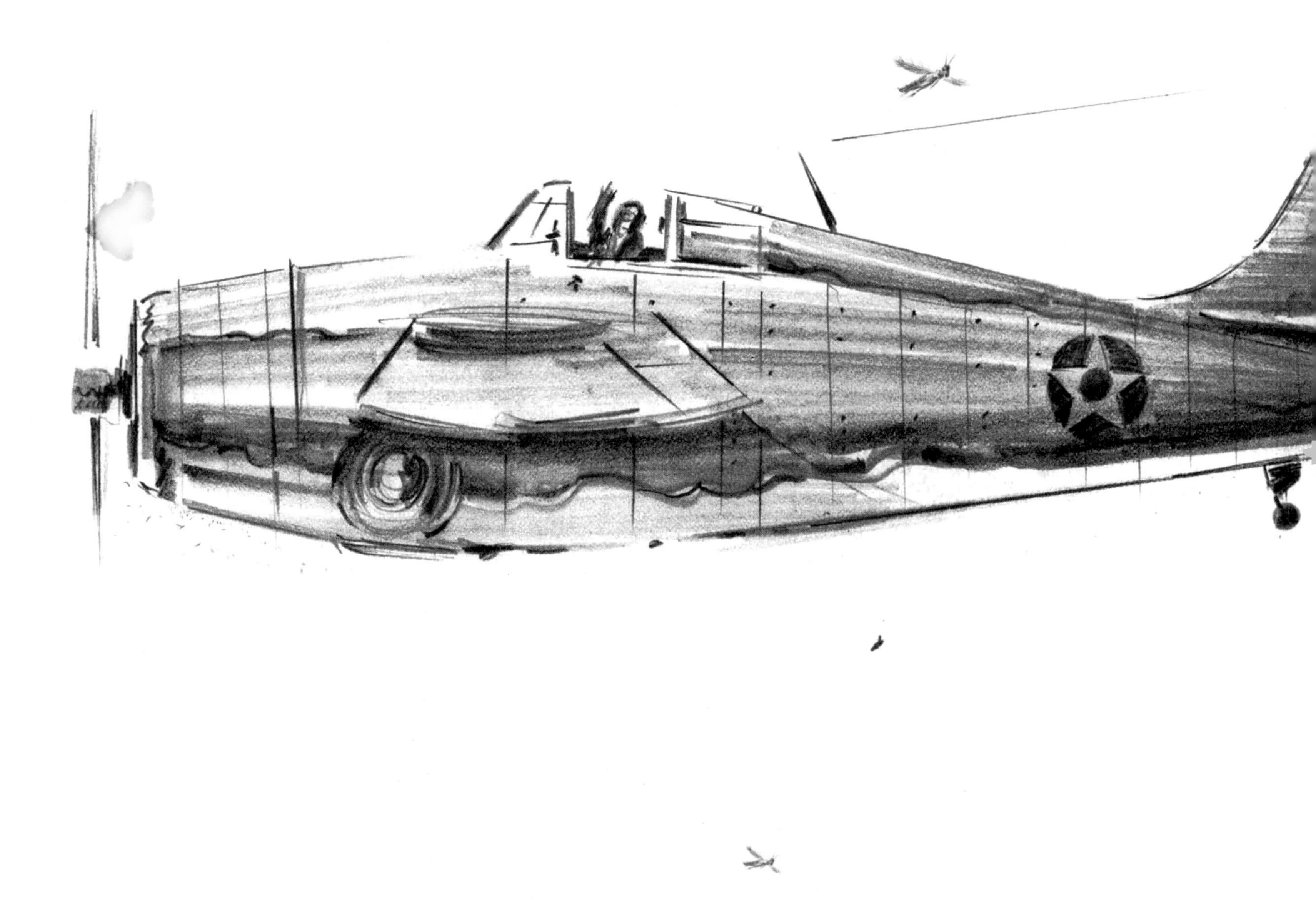

We were a small part of Aviation history that day. It wasn't until years later we found out what we had witnessed.

Grumman aircraft had upgraded the"Wildcat" to a much improved version they called the "Hellcat." Juicy was one of many pilots sent from the combat zone to be briefed on this remarkable upgrade. Lake Michigan ore boats became makeshift aircraft carriers on which the pilots took off and landed. With improved speed, armament and firepower the Japanese Zero was outclassed in every way. At first glance Japanese pilots mistook the new "Hellcat" for the old "Wildcat." The result was 100% fatal. 5,271 Japanese lost their lives because they didn't know the difference.

With a major war on his mind, Julius Brownstein finally said the "good-bye" he never had time to say.

VILLAINS, VICTORS & VICTIMS .

Every Saturday afternoon the first three rows of the Liberty Theater were filled with kids from six to thirteen. It smelled of popcorn, Milk Duds and if you sat near a farm kid, manure.

Mr. King , the theater manager, had more than his hands full with this charged up group. He'd make examples of a few older kids, throwing them out by the nap of their necks. Then they'd sneak back in by walking backwards up the Exit stairs and be back in their seats before the lights dimmed.

When the MGM Lion growled the theater became dead silent. We forgave the cheap quality of the film and loved the shallow plot of the weekly propaganda War Movies. They were the bad guys, we the good guys. We'd cheer when the American boys heroically manned their aircraft and jeer when the sinister music clearly defined the bad guys.

I watched the "dogfight" reflected in Gerry Ellis's glasses. The crowd erupted in cheers as the burning Messerschmitt spiraled downward into oblivion. "You asked for it, you dirty Kraut !" Danny Manthe screamed ! "Danny, aren't you a Kraut ?" I asked innocently He stared at me as if I were a farm kid.

A loud collective groan filled the theater. The tables were turning . A Messerschmitt had maneuvered its way unto our hero's tail. There was always a close- up of spitting German machine guns followed by bullets ripping in to the metal of the American aircraft. My heart was now in my mouth. A small cheer went up as the parachute of the American pilot opened. The distant German plane began banking slowly then headed towards our pilot. The popcorn munching stopped. Gerry Ellis's eyes were as round as his glasses. I couldn't watch as the face of the German gloated at the sight of the American hanging helplessly. Did I see fangs as the German drooled with delight ? I buried my face in my brother's shoulder. "He'll never shoot him! He has no airplane now! He's harmless! Don't shoot!" I begged.

The first box of popcorn headed for the screen as the German opened fire. The American twitched and twisted as the bullets ripped through his entire body. A barrage of popcorn boxes along with a few Milk Duds and a chorus of profanity filled the air when the German's gloating face filled the screen.

This was a standard scene in every movie. The only variable was when the German was replaced by that sneaky dreaded Jap, "Tokyo Joe!"

Not one word was spoken as we walked home. We stopped at the Hall Park Bridge. Then sat on the edge watching the oil soaked waters of Ox Creek disappear under the bridge.

Someone broke out a pack of Pall Mall extra length cigarettes. Finally, the silence erupted into a screamfest..
"Those dirty Germans! He gunned a helpless man."
" It's just a phony movie." Rudy Polstin answered.
"Not all Germans are like that!"

The older guys did the talking. I did take a puff off a Pall Mall. " What about the news reel ?" the discussion continued. "Those storm troopers goose stepping into every town in Europe? That was as real as it gets !"
"What about the sneaky Jap bastards ?" Someone offered.
"What about the Italians?" another asked.
"When they run out of spaghetti they surrender."
Someone answered. "At least they don't hit you when you're asleep on Sunday." I countered.
" Look what they did to the Jews.' Billy Kritt said quietly.
A huge puff of smoke went up at the though of that.

Out of the silence came a small voice.
"What about Tokyo Joe?" Little Ronnie Ellis asked.
"He's a bastard too."
"No Ronnie, he's an actor and you're too young to say bastard. Now give me that cigarette." Donnie said.

The discussion went on until the last cigarette butt floated down the mighty Ox Creek. We did resolve a few things however. The war was real and our boys were dying. Also, if the war continues, it will be our turn to fight these dastardly bastards!

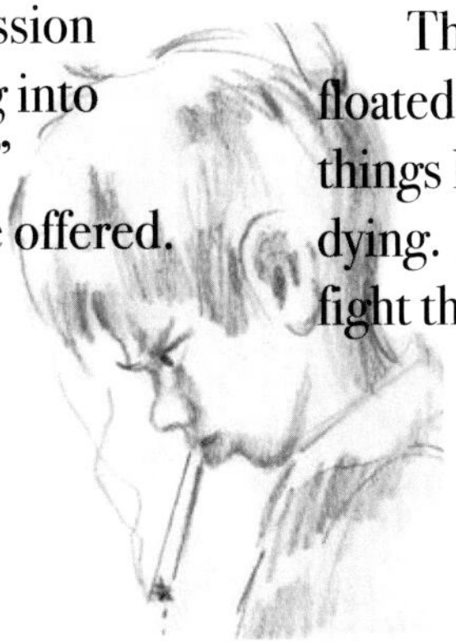

I awoke to the slurping sounds of my father eating oatmeal. It must be at least six A.M. I thought. I had tossed and turned all night after hearing the news. The almighty German Reich was crumbling on all fronts. German prisoners were arriving stateside. Last nights News Palladium announced that about a thousand prisoners were heading to the Benton Harbor Naval Armory! I could barely swallow my coffee soaked saltine crackers, that's only a block away!

My brother Vince and I took the short cut down the alley joining a group of trumped-up kids. The army that had dogged the world were here in our neighborhood ! I strutted confidently down the alley, but the truth was if anyone even whisperd "Heil Hitler!" I'd turn and run to mama.

When we approached the rim of Hall Park Hill, some kids were already posturing. "Those dirty rotten Krauts are gonna get a piece of my mind." Someone threatened. "Hey Yampolski, give em' a piece of your mind in Yiddish!" Someone else offered.

As we approached the Bivouac area our determined stride shortened. American soldiers armed to the teeth with machine guns were everywhere. Their faces were somber as they went about the business at hand. No longer boys, now trained killers... standing on the very spot we played war games !

The Naval armory was at the foot of Hall Park Hill. From a distance you could see the German prisoners in a makeshift compound. An entire city block had been cordoned off by barbed wire. Machine guns were in place at

intervals along the fence. Gulp, maybe I should have slept in.

The American armed guards gave me all the courage I needed. I slowly approached the barbed wire compound. The prisoners were playing soccer, most were shirtless. I'd never seen a ball go that high. Of course I'd never seen a soccer game before.

They were as curious as we were. Slowly, they approached us.

They were't men at all! They were small and scrawny boys! Their shirtless chests revealed no hair. Some were barely pubescent! Our age! Donnie Richmond was older them some of them!

Were these frightened children the storm troopers that terrorized the world ? The dastardly monsters we saw at the Liberty Theater ?
Good God! They looked like the Popke boys! The Conrad's! Danny Manthe!

"Back away from that fence!" a guard barked. I'd never been yelled at by a man carrying a weapon before, let alone one fully loaded.
I think I soiled my brother's underwear I borrowed this morning.

What maniac would send these kids into battle ? The sour taste of saltine crackers and coffee filled my mouth and nose. It was more than my stomach could handle.
I headed for home.

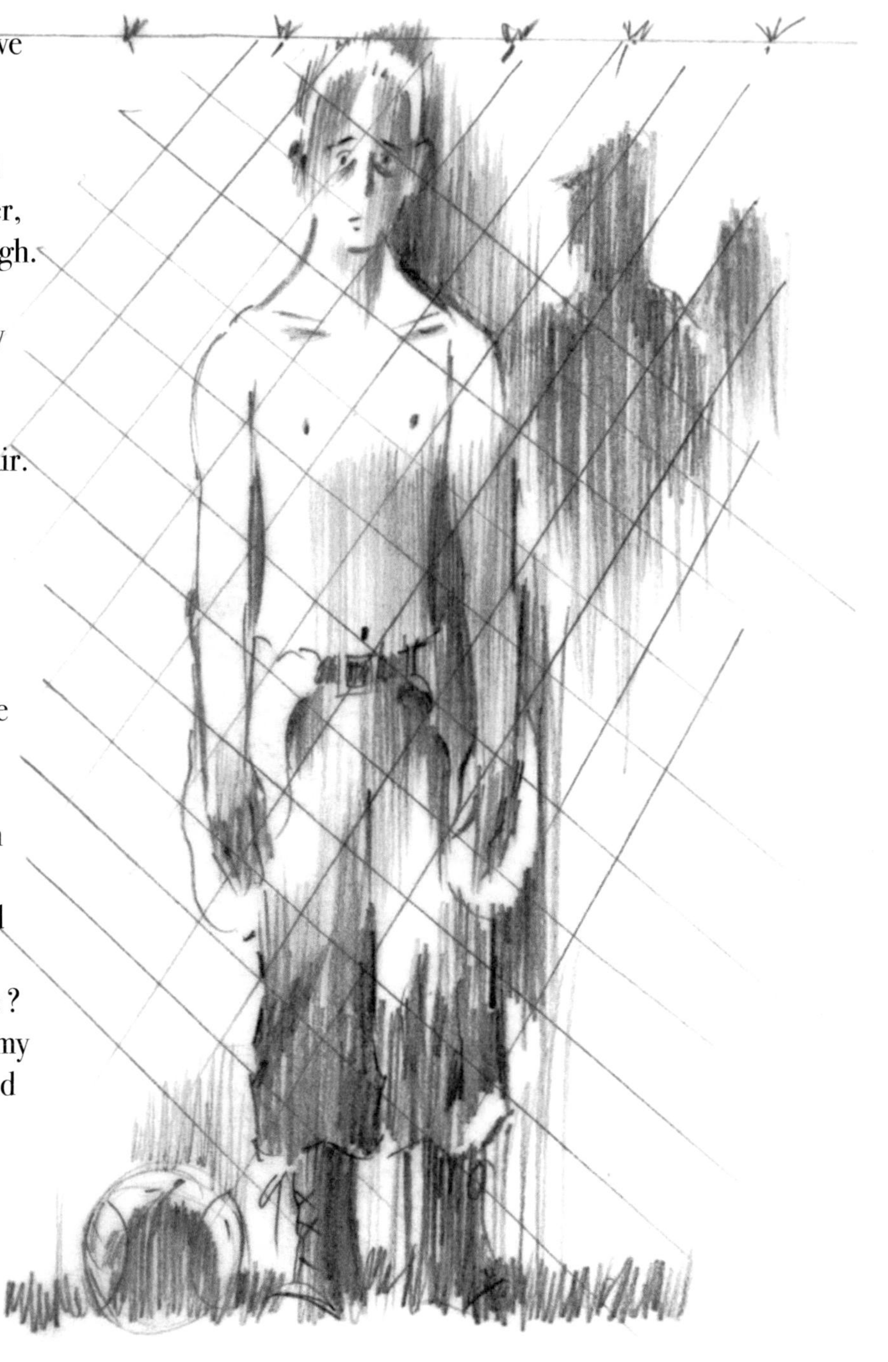

I sat quietly at the dinner table that evening. We all listened to my fathers impromptu grace. He gave the usual kudos for the zucchini, waxed eloquently about the ravioli, then he paused and looked up at the kitchen ceiling, shrugged his shoulders and said.
"JesusaChrist! Will you please enda this Godamma war ?"
I spilled my milk.

Yes, he did it again. Yes, he used the Lord's name in vain. Then I thought it through, If anyone could get away with this it would be Vincenzo. I looked up at his kind face, smiled, and passed him the zucchini.

In the evening the entire town would gather at the Naval Armory. When the German prisoners finished playing soccer they would gather in a huge formation, lock arms and sing.

I watched as a sea of young German faces sang with amazing bravado. I was overwhelmed. I'd never heard acappella singing in a group this large before.

I didn't understand the lyrics, but I did detect words like "Heart, Home and Motherland." Words I'd picked up from Danny Manthe's daily German lessons.

As their voices drifted up into the warm night air, tears ran down their bare chests. It was then we all

realized it. They were frightened homesick children! My mother, not understanding German lyrics but familar with human pain, starred glassy eyed. Our German neighbors wept openly.

The next day Slosson's Bar, dance hall and grocery store was out of candy bars and chewing gum. American guards stood aghast as Baby Ruths, Old Henrys and Three Musketeer candy bars filled the air. Young German prisoners scrambled like kids at an Easter egg hunt. One prisoner nodded to me, smiled thankfully, then bit into the Baby Ruth I had flung over the barbed wire fence.

As the feeding frenzy continued, an unsettlement came over me. Aside from the group there was a mature German prisoner . His cold blue eyes assessed every move I made. He had full thick neck, blond hair and a trim waist. The perfect poster for the Aryan race Adolph Hitler himself spoke of. I tried desperately to convince myself he was looking at someone else. When he slowly raised his hand and pointed between my eyes there was no doubt. Then he slowly raised his hand to his mouth and faked a long drag on an imaginary cigarette.
Then slowly, without expression, he faked an exhale.
Hoping to deflect his obvious command, I nervously looked around for someone else he may be gesturing towards.
Then he clarified my marching orders. He firmly locked his eyes with mine then impatiently flicked his head twice towards Slosson's.

It didn't take much to convince my friend that my ass was on the line and I was back in no time with a pack of "Luckies" cigarettes.

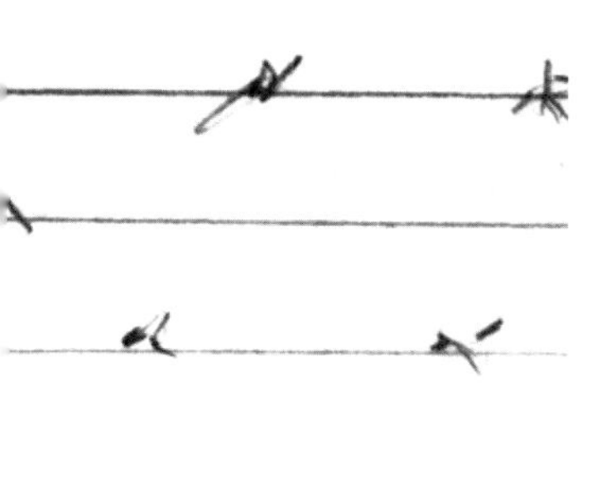

When I approached the compound he was waiting.
So was the American guard.
"Listen to me kid." he growled. "This is war. I've seen what these bastards can do .They are the enemy ! They would kill us given half the the chance. I've seen it."
"Now take those cigarettes you're hiding behind your back home to your father ! Got it ?" I nodded affirmative.

As the guard left for his appointed rounds he kept one eye on me. The German's cold blue eyes never blinked.

There was a desperation in them I'd never seen before.
I was between a man with a loaded Thompson Machine Gun and a man that desperately needed a cigarette !
What do I do?

I took the safe choice !
I flung the pack of Lucky Strikes over the barbed wire fence and was at the top of Hall Park hill before they landed at the German prisoners feet.

The Shyman family lived at the top of a hill facing the second floor window of the Naval Armory. Their back porch faced the Galley where food was prepared for the prisoners. Each day Mrs. Shyman and a German cook would chat in German. One afternoon the cook flipped a message to her using a large rubber band as a sling shot. Before she could open the note, her kitchen was filled with American troops barring Thompson machine guns. She quickly slipped it safely into the cleavage between her large bosoms. When interrogated about it she plead ignorance. Ready to do battle to protect the contents of the note, she only answered in German. "ich verstehe nicht! ich verstehe nicht!" (I don't understand. I don't understand.) she repeated. Finally, in frustration the Americans left. These were the boys that brought the almighty German Army to its knees in North Africa, in full retreat on the rocky beaches of Italy, but this was a battle they knew they'd never win.

I often wonder about all this. Who were the villains in this war ? Were they the fifteen year old Germans that cried themselves to sleep on the basketball court of the Naval Armory ? Or were they the American boys trained to kill at the drop of a paper note ? And who are victors ? Maybe nobody really won this war. One thing is sure . We were all victims.

Regarding the cryptic note hidden away in Mrs. Shyman's cleavage? The contents remained a secret for years, then the truth finally leaked out.

It was a strudel recipe.

REST & RECUPERATION.

The setting summer sun forced long shadows from the pup tents along the ridge of Hall Park Hill. Donnie and I sat on a concrete wall built during The Great Depression. We watched as our troops settled in after a hard day guarding the German prisoners.

"The Germans get to sleep inside, our boys have to sleep outside." I observed.

A cheer went up as two trucks loaded with women soldiers stopped at the encampment.

"You can't feel too sorry for our boys , look who they get to sleep with." Donnie winked.

They were the Women's Army Corps. Women soldiers equally in need of a well earned night off. Hardly thirteen and pretending to understand Donnie's remark, I winked back.

We watched as the sun sunk behind the forest of of hugh oak trees at the bottom of Hall Park hill.

US

As night set in the laughter grew louder, and drunker. We squinted to see the action to no avail. The crowd was now in full silhouette, the light from their cigarettes moved like fireflies in the dark. The boisterous banter of the crowd slowly settled down into soft whispers.

Donnie was unusually silent. Then he looked me straight in the face and raised one eyebrow. He always did that when he had a wild idea.

"Tell me when they're on," he whispered as he headed into the small bushes surrounding the nearby manhole cover.

I followed and watched as he disappeared down the manhole. I was puzzled, why would he ....

"Are the sprinklers on ?" Donnie's voice echoed up from the manhole. I stood on the concrete wall and watched in horror as the crowd erupted in an Indian rain dance. Screeching and swearing as they leaped.

" They're on! They're on!" I screamed.

"There they are! There they are! It's those damn kids!" the soldiers bellowed as they headed towards us.

I wasn't the fastest kid in the block, but no one could have touched me that night. Especially a garrison of soldiers with their pants down around their ankles.

I'm sure that when their grandkids ask "Grandpa, what did you do in the war ?" They'll never tell this story.

BLITZKRIEGS & BULGES.

"Ahhhh, there's sad news tonight!" he moaned. Gabriel Heater, the old pessimist, was at it again. Scaring the daylights out of my father. What could be so sad ? The last I heard was, the Japanese and Germans were in full retreat. My father, dazed and confused, sat stared blankly at the pulsing orange light on our radio. I listened as Mr. Heater continued. The Germans had launched a massive counterattack and had just regained a huge amount of French and Belgium ground. My father, like a frightened child, turned to me and said " I no reada so good, Genie." as he handed me the evening news paper.

A large map of Europe filled the front page. A big red arrow signifying German troop movements had pierced the black dotted front line forming a hugh bulge. The battle of Ardennes Forest was now referred to as the"Battle of the Bulge." "Jeeze!" I thought as crawled up on my fathers lap. This is terrible news.

Mr. Heater wasn't exaggerating. How can I sugarcoat this for my frightened father ? I was now the parent and my father the child.

Carefully, I pointed to all the smaller black arrows representing the Allied Armies. I confidently explained our strengths. Carefully avoiding any mention of the hugh territory the Germans had reclaimed. Methodically I droned on, wandering somewhere between the truth and wishful thinking.
Some people might call it lying.
Nevertheless, my father was snoring peacefully at nine thirty.
Right on schedule for his six o'clock wake up call.

Thanksgiving dinner was shrouded by the continuing bad news from the front. A blanket of fog lingered over the battle field grounding our air support. This allowed massive German troop movements to run freely through France and Belgium.

Back home at the dinner table, my father stuttered through his traditional ad-lib grace. The room was silent hoping for just a shred of levity but it never came. The only movement in the room was a tiny fruit fly that lazily circled the dinner table.

We all watched as it slowly found its way to my father's wine glass. All our eyes were now on the tiny fruit fly as it hovered over the glass of wine. Than it lowered itself down into the glass. Then, after one whiff , it disappeared. My father shrugged his shoulders and said "Nobody likesa my wine."

It was the comic relief we needed. We all eagerly dug into the magnificent meal.

There was the traditional squabble over the wishbone and the jokes about who most deserves the turkey butt. Every one laughed, except Theresa.

She sat, baby in lap, staring silently at the untouched plate of turkey, sweet potatoes and green beans in front of her. Her mind obviously two thousand miles away.

She hadn't received a letter from Jack since he left England. That was months ago.

The traditional neighborhood Thanksgiving football game was postponed. The reason: The down and dreary doldrums.

The newsreels that played between the movies still haunt me. Mud splattered faces of American boys slogging through the freezing rain in Belgium. Faces with a dazed exhaustion only extreme fatigue can cause.

The temperature was below freezing and the battle was heating up. I shivered as I watched our troops living in fox holes dug from frozen tundra.
I huddled for warmth against my brother in the seat next to me.

Then there were the German corpses. Mouth agape, caught in the midst of a scream. Sometimes I would look down at my goulashes until the newsreel ended.

The December sun was setting earlier as we headed home. Main street was now deserted except for one lone soldier and his duffle bag. Obviously in transit and totally disoriented.

He was slight of build and frightened. Not at all the soldier Hollywood so heroically portrays. Meek and mild mannered, I could never imagine him in the newsreel we just saw.

He was the type some people called Cannon Fodder. "Most likely to succeed in dying in battle." they would add with a laugh. This was too close to the truth to be funny, I thought sadly.

He had missed his bus so we took him home with us. My mother was always skeptical of unfamiliar guests, but welcomed him warmly. This war had waived all former protocol.

He barely uttered a word as he inhaled his only home cooking in months. My brother and I watched, head resting on elbows, as color began to return to his face.

We never asked his name, where he was from or where he was going. It didn't matter. What mattered was he left with a smile and a piece of apple pie for the road.

Years have gone by since that evening and I rarely pass that corner. But whenever I do, I still see that that frightened boy.
I hope he made it through the war.
I hope he told this story to his grandchildren.

As Christmas approached, 'The Battle of the Bulge" intensified. The song of the day was "White Christmas." It was a sentiment spawned from our fighting forces in the South Pacific. Tired of deep green jungles and unbearable heat, they could only dream of snow.

For different reasons, it was the sentiment our fly boys were praying for . Their prayers were answered. The temperature dropped , the fog lifted and a most welcome snowfall began. With the targets now clear of fog, massive air attacks began. Bombs pounded the advancing Panzer tanks stopping them in their iron tracks. The battlefield was now shrouded in a blanket of blood splattered snow. Tenacious American troops held their ground against superior mechanized forces.

Sgt. Jack Palmer was in the thick of it. More than once he was rousted from his foxhole only to return and personally evict German soldiers from it with hand grenades. The seesaw battle continued for

weeks. On one return he found his rosary he left behind in pieces. Obviously, a Lutheran extremist.

On one occasion three German soldiers returned to the foxhole with the assumption that the trench was still theirs. Unaware that Jack was still in it. They were met point blank by one shot from Jack's M-1 rifle. One Armor piercing 38 caliber bullet left three Germans dead.

Jack mumbled when he told this story.

Under his breath, as if he were really telling himself.

I remember him saying "I dug the hole, dammit!" Groping to find even a shred of justification for what had just happened.

Most would celebrate such a valliant effort. A script worthy of John Wayne, to say the least.

But to Jack, it was the burden of guilt he would carry for the rest of his life.

WAR & PEACE ON EARTH.

The winter deep freeze came early back home. We'd been living without meat, sugar and other staples. To make matters worse, my mother announced that there was shortage of money, therefore, Christmas would be just another day on the calendar. Yes, there would be baccala, squid, clams, anchovies and walnuts with linguini. Everything a kid would never want to eat. That included no gifts, no hanging stockings and no Christmas tree! That made it a given that there would be no Santa Claus.

I was crushed, my brother Vince seemed indifferent about the whole thing.

The News-Palladium newspaper didn't help. Every day they would taunt. Only six...five...four shopping days 'til Christmas. I was beside myself, my brother remained oblivious.
Jeez! Didn't he realize the impact this would leave on our lives forever ?

On the day before Christmas my brother calmly said "Don't worry, Ma will give in.
She always gives in."

I went to the closet and checked out the ornament box. I found the pear, the broken star, the miniature snow covered houses, the entire nativity scene including the three legged cow. Even the wooden match stick that my dad substituted for the fourth leg was still firmly in place. But there was nothing to hang the ornaments on! The lights! Where do we put the three legged cow ? The broken star ? This could be our most disastrous Christmas ever!

There were no visions of sugar plumbs dancing in my head that Christmas Eve. I stared mindlessly at the crack in our bedroom ceiling. My eyes were as wide as saucers. Don't bother listening for tiny reindeer paws on our roof. Why would they ever bother to stop at a dark house ? The only other dark house in the block will be the Kritt's. But they don't celebrate Christmas. They're Jewish.

My father's snore was now a steady purr. That meant it was now just after midnight. That's when a dark silhouette appeared in the bedroom doorway . It was someone wearing a hat, a scarf, a heavy mackinaw with an ax over his shoulder. Was it that German prisoner craving another cigarette ? I could have cared less. The damage was done. This nightmare couldn't get any worse than it already is. Go ahead, chop away!

It was my brother Vince." Get dressed! It's colder than a witches tit out there." he whispered.

The temperature was well below zero. The hardened snow squeaked under our feet. To this day I still hate that sound. The snowflakes were now turning to ice crystals. Vince kept a quick determined pace. I struggled to keep up. We left the last street light at Thresher and headed into the darkness of Hull Avenue.

There was someone lying helter skelter in a snow bank just ahead. "Hi Duddey," Vince said, nonchalantly. Duddey flashed a big inebriated smile then waved as we passed.

When we reached the rim of Hall Park hill, a cutting wind rushed up to meet us. I thought of our boys in the trenches sleeping in this every night. Always with one eye opened. I wish I was home freezing in our frigid little bedroom.

As we descended into the deep ravine hobo fires grew disturbingly closer. The rail road that followed frozen Ox Creek was definitely out of bounds. Let alone after midnight. Definitely off limits ! Vince was relentless as he plowed ahead into the building snow storm.

When we reached a stand of trees, my brother stopped. He grabbed a small tree like it was a turkeys neck and was about to behead it. "What about this ?" he asked.

I didn't answer. Then he grabbed another tree. "How about this?" he barked. My eyes were glassy. I couldn't see through the blinding whiteout.

He grabbed a third tree. Now impatient, he screamed. "SAY SOMETHING !"

I knew that "yes" would be a death sentence for the tiny tree. My tongue was tied. Then I heard four sickening chops and the tree crashed to earth.

There was a long silent pause. A short moment of guilt.....followed by terror of what we did.

We took off running, Vince dragging the freshly killed tree, me the ax.

My heart pounded out of my chest. Why was I running ? Then it sunk in, I was an accomplice !

We quickly reached the rim of the hill where duddey was now sitting up. Grief! I thought. "Duddey was eye witnessed to the whole thing! He cheered then clapped as we passed. I was relieved. Duddey wasn't the squealing type.

We reached our darkened home in record time. The tree was a sassafras. A deciduous tree that loses all its foliage in the fall. Not the kind you see in the ads next to the Coca-Cola Santa Claus.

When we put it upright on our handmade stand we gasped. It resembled a prehistoric fish skeleton. Vince silently glared at me as he made a makeshift stand.

The string of lights helped. The ornaments and two packages of last years tinsel added to the cause, but it still looked like a giant fishbone. A giant fishbone with ornaments. Seven sheets of green manilla paper, a scissors and a bowl of homemade paste and a lovely paper chain adorned our masterpiece.

It was the wee hours of the morning now. Our four posted bed was a welcome sight. With the wall on my left, my big brother guarding my right, I felt safe from everything, except for that blankety-blank chain smoking German lurking under our bed.

I woke to the slurping sound of my father eating hot oatmeal in the adjacent kitchen. Wonderful cooking smells filled our bedroom.We raced to the front room to see if the big fat guy delivered. Yes, there were presents, but I don't remember mentioning socks and underwear. Somewhere between downtown Benton Harbor and the North Pole old booze breath must have lost the Christmas list.

The dining room table was filled with magnificence. My father smiled so broadly the gapping hole left by an errant olive pit appeared. My Mother had her game face on as she went about her chores. I did see her face light up when I caught her trying to steal a glance at my brother and I. It was that adoring look only a proud mom could have when she realizes her tiny boys had just learned one of life's important lessons.

When life doesn't go your way, don't cry about it. Find the testicles to go out and do something about it.

Back in Belgium foes on both sides put aside their weapons in reverence to the birth of Christ. The war was silent that night.

It remains my favorite Christmas.

A shotgun blast into the midnight sky welcomed in the new year. A right of passage into manhood I never understood.

When it was my turn I cringed. The 16 gage hunting shotgun smelled of burning sulfur. "Cock it, dummy!" My brother yelled as he reached in and clicked the hammer back. The gun went off immediately as my nervous finger choked the trigger. I know it scared him more than it scared me.

I still shutter when I think of the angry sound those shot gun blasts made. A small reminder of the sounds our boys were living with day and night. Only

they were machine gun bullets, mortar shells, and the dreaded 88 millimeter shells. Not aimed skyward, but directly at them.

The goose stepping boots that filled our newsreels were now back on their heels. Sgt. Jack Palmer was one of many chasing them. His company, now on German soil, was preparing to take a rail line. As his platoon approached the rail line they ran into a convoy of German Panzer tanks moving slowly down a road.

He ordered his men to take cover behind a pile of stream crossing culverts. Jack was face down in the snow, praying that the German tank commander had not spotted his platoon position.

One massive tank in the convoy groaned to a halt. The long silence was deafening. Then a grinding sound broke the silence as the giant turret began to slowly turn. The storied 88 millimeter anti aircraft gun stopped point blank at Jack's platoon. The deafening blast shook the earth all the way to Jack's position. The shell, designed to explode in a hundred pieces, landed into the pile of culverts. One piece of shrapnel about an inch long, ripped through the flimsy culvert, into Jack's chest just to the left his heart, exiting out his back. I hope he felt no pain.

I remember Theresa's shriek when she spotted the Western Union messenger approach our front porch. I met him at the door. He had an olive drab uniform, a tiny hat with a short stubby leather bill and matching leather chaps. "Mrs. Jack A. Palmer ?" he methodically asked as he handed me the message. I looked towards Theresa, now unconscious, then took the telegram.

My mother read the letter then calmly tried to revive Theresa. My small hands tremble as I read the message. It looked like a ransom note. A scramble of words seemed cut out and pasted across the page. I can't believe this is happening. My heart was in my mouth I was fearing the worst. Officially and unemotionally the message read:

YOUR HUSBAND JACK A. PALMER
HAS BEEN SERIOUSLY WOUNDED IN ACTION.

I breathed a hugh sigh of relief. "Thank God he's alive!" I thought.

I rushed to Theresa, now conscious but still dazed. "Theresa! It's good news!" I said with a huge smile. "He's only seriously wounded!"

Her eyes rolled back. She fainted again .

As it ended up, I was right. There was cause for great joy. Jack would be home soon.

CARS HONKED,
SIRENS WAILED & THE
FAT LADY SANG.

It was over ! Finally, America had awakened from a long nightmare. Kate Smith, our portly sweetheart of song belted out "God Bless America" over all three networks.
Air alert sirens wailed and babies cried. I could feel my heart pound as I headed for the News Palladium.

News boys clamored and shoved as they received their bundle of newspapers. "JAPS QUIT ! WAR IN PACIFIC OVER!" the headline shouted.

I could smell the still wet ink as I folded my newspapers. I filled my basket then peddled to the top of Highland Hill where my route began.

A loud cheer went up when they saw me. My customers were out in the streets and on their porches eagerly awaiting the news. They welcomed me with open arms, some hugged, others patted my small shoulders as if I single handedly ended the war.

Mrs. Glazer blurted out her feelings in German as she squeezed my hands. Harriet, her voluptuous daughter, gave me her traditional breast press. Then a husky laugh. Tony D., an Italian beer distributor, shoved a handful of folding money in my shirt pocket then grabbed an armful of newspapers.

The Kraft house was understandably silent. The gold star on the flag in the window explained it all. Mr. Kraft emerged, handed me a dime for his paper, then disappeared back in his darkened house.
Mrs. Kraft never came out.

I returned home sagging under the weight of bulging pockets filled with quarters, dimes and nickels, staggered by what I just saw.

We were people who grew up in extremely different cultures, who barely understood each other's language, but put our differences aside for the common good of our country.
Our enemies never had a chance.

My budding ego couldn't help but believe that our airplane club had an important part in this long awaited Victory. After all, not one enemy plane dared to venture into our no-fly zone.

The world gave an enormous sigh of relief that night. Even my chain smoking nemesis under our bed purred like a baby.

THE END